KU-216-184

This book belongs to:

....

....

Age: ....

Fancy dress: ....

My scariest face!

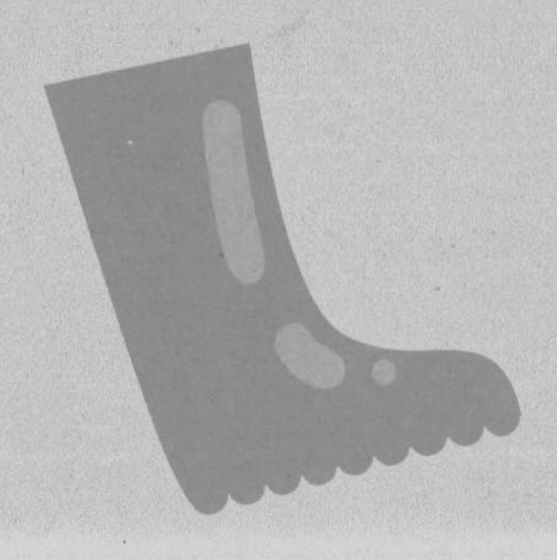

For Sophie and all the other puddle jumpers!

– Kim

Published by b small publishing ltd.
www.bsmall.co.uk

1 2 3 4 5 ISBN 978-1-912909-91-9

Text, design and illustrations by Kim Hankinson.
Editorial by Sam Hutchinson. Cover design by Vicky Barker.

Printed in China by WKT Co. Ltd.

British Library Cataloguing-in-Publication Data.
A catalogue record for this book is available from the British Library.

Activities for ...

leaf-kicking, pumpkin-carving, trick-or-treating ... AUTUMN NUTS!

Kim Hankinson

HOW TO USE THIS BOOK

This book is full of daring-looking-thinking-listening activities everyone can try. Starting on any page, do as many activities as you can fit into a day and in any order you like.

The activities are colour-coded to help you choose what sort of activity you would like to do. Match the activity key below with the coloured circle in the contents list opposite or the coloured circle enclosing each page number. There are extra pages for notes and doodles throughout the book.

Have fun and enjoy a wickedly wonderful autumn!

ACTIVITY KEY

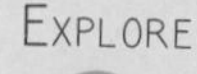

Always ask an adult when you see a red warning symbol.

CONTENTS CHECKLIST:

FANCY ONES

LOT-O-LEGS!

BUG HUNT

It is a great time to spot creepy-crawlies. How many types can you find?

Feathered friends

Food is hard to find in colder months. Some birds fly south, so leave food out for those who stay at home!

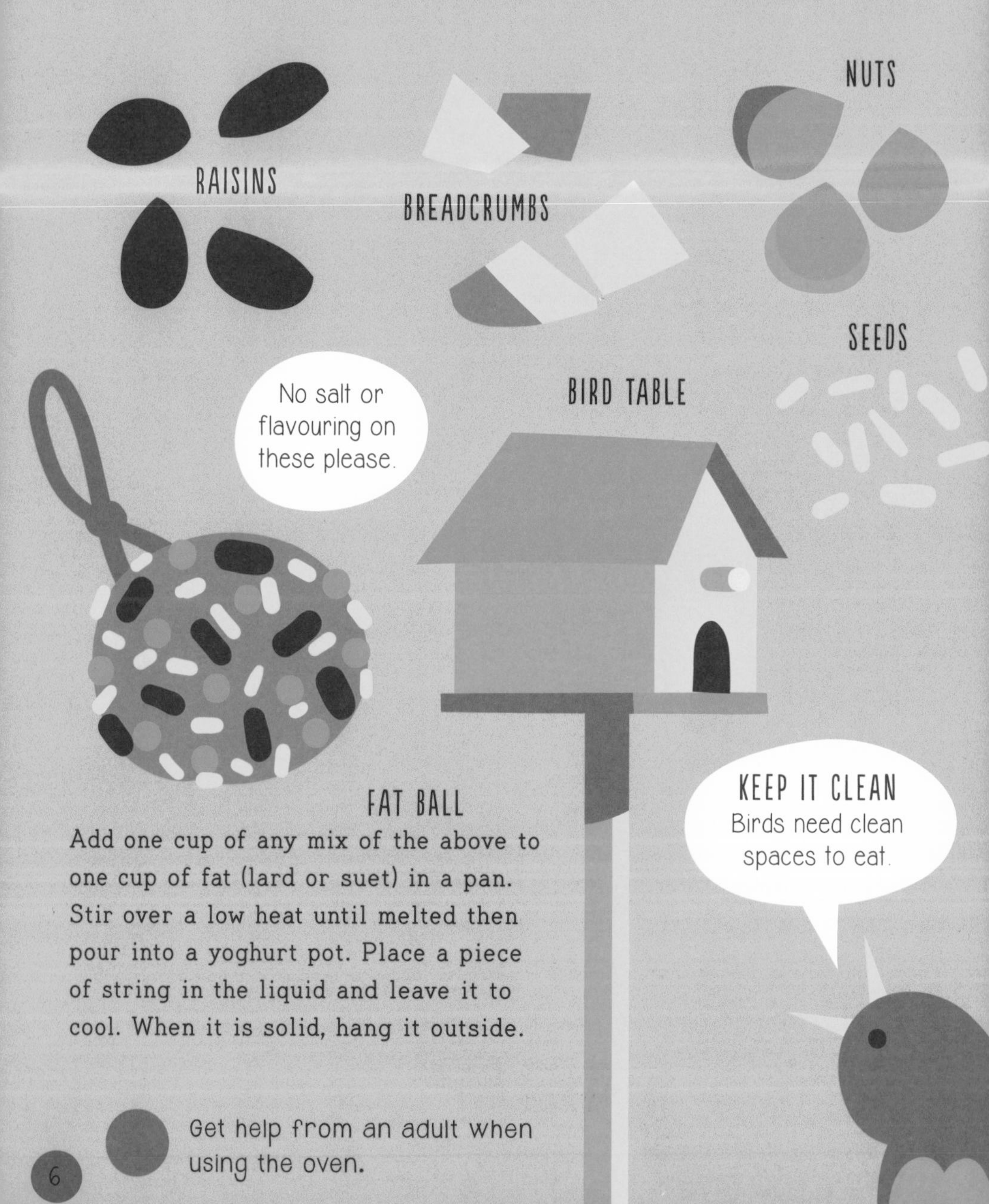

FAT BALL

Add one cup of any mix of the above to one cup of fat (lard or suet) in a pan. Stir over a low heat until melted then pour into a yoghurt pot. Place a piece of string in the liquid and leave it to cool. When it is solid, hang it outside.

Get help from an adult when using the oven.

Bird spotter

Look for birds outside a window. Colour the bird shapes to match all the ones you spot.

Autumn colours

Collect a palette of autumnal colours.

Here are a couple to get you started.

SQUIRREL'S TAIL

AUTUMN SKY

DAILY DARE

SHHHH! Whether you are trying to spot animals or creep up on someone for a Halloween surprise, you will need to be quiet. Practise these ninja moves.

Home sweet home!

Make some safe spaces outside where animals can shelter from the coming winter.

STICK BUNDLE

Place sticks and twigs in a pile at the edge of a garden or park to make a great shelter for bugs and small animals.

POT STACK

If you stack pots facing down somewhere sheltered, you will give bees somewhere cosy to hide from the frost.

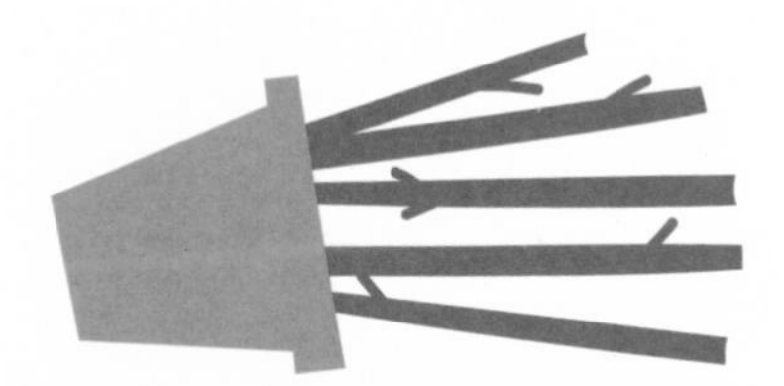

POT AND STICKS

Place a pot on its side and fill it with sticks to make another great shelter.

BED OF LEAVES

Collect leaves and put them under a hedge somewhere quiet. This will make a very cosy sleeping place for small hibernating creatures.

BAT-MOBILE

Create a mobile using the bat template below.

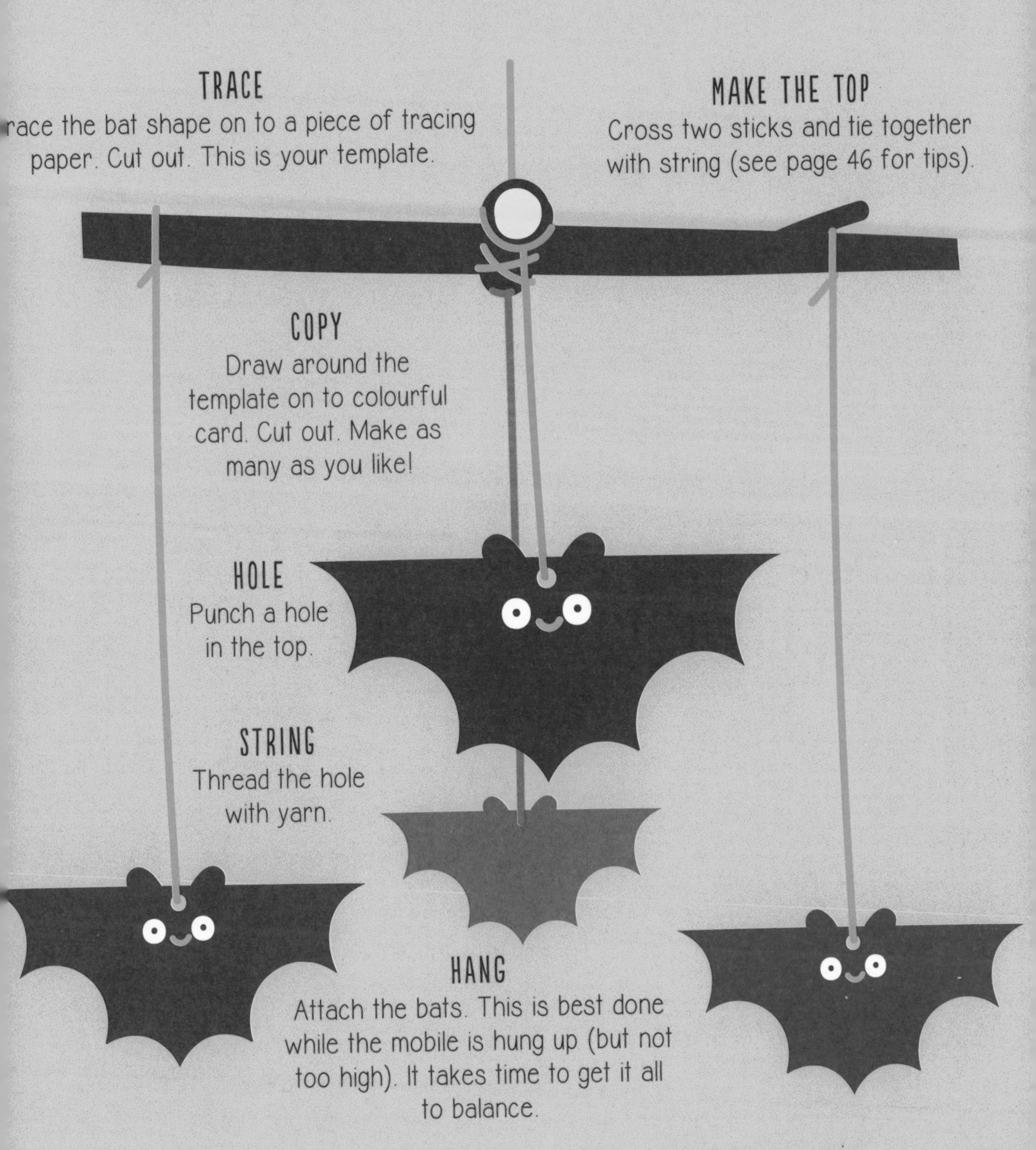

TRACE

Trace the bat shape on to a piece of tracing paper. Cut out. This is your template.

MAKE THE TOP

Cross two sticks and tie together with string (see page 46 for tips).

COPY

Draw around the template on to colourful card. Cut out. Make as many as you like!

HOLE

Punch a hole in the top.

STRING

Thread the hole with yarn.

HANG

Attach the bats. This is best done while the mobile is hung up (but not too high). It takes time to get it all to balance.

VOILÀ-AH-HA-HÀ!

Changing colours

Autumn is full of changing colours. Try seeing your world in a different colour!

1. Draw a scene but do not add any shading or colour yet. You can use a new colouring in sheet that you have not started colouring in, if you do not like drawing.

2. Pick ten colouring pens or pencils that go with your scene.

3. Colour the rectangle (body) of each pencil below with one of your chosen colours.

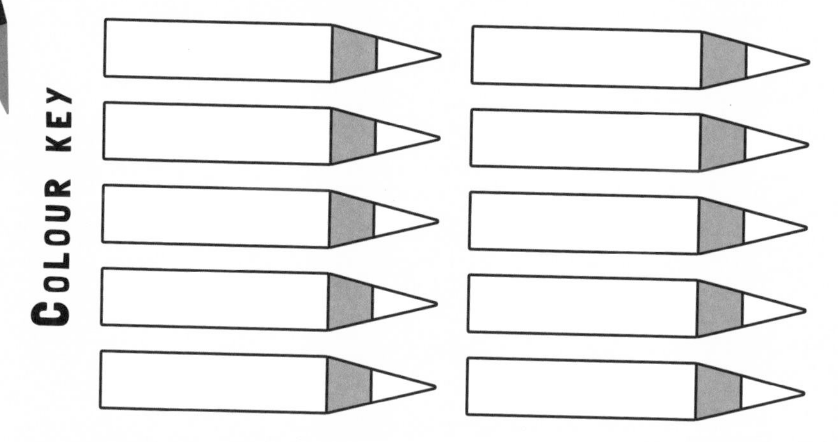

4. Now switch up the palette! Colour the triangle (nib) of each pencil with a different colour.

5. You are ready to colour! Instead of colouring things as they should be, use the key and swap each colour for the different colour in the nib of the pencil. Do this with each colour for a truly groovy piece of artwork.

Time capsule

Time to swap your summer togs for winter ones. As you put them away, sneak in a note or a toy, something that will make you smile when you open it up next year.

Mushroom spotters

Can you spot these fungi? It is good for the habitat to leave them in place. So take a picture instead!

WARNING

Never eat or touch wild mushrooms without permission as they can be poisonous.

Denim of the Dead

In celebration of the *Día de los Muertos* and Halloween, try this skull pattern.

You will need

PEN
SCISSORS
PAPER
OLD CLOTHING
PAINTBRUSH
FABRIC PAINTS
PENCIL WITH RUBBER END

1. Copy the skull design on to any size paper you like and cut out. This is your stencil.
2. Using your stencil, draw the skull shape on to the old clothing. You can do lots or just one.
3. Paint the inside of the skull in one colour. Wait to dry.
4. Using the rubber end of the pencil, dot fabric paint in contrasting colours on and around the skull. Experiment!

Feeling windy

Try these easy ways to watch the wind!

OTHER SENSES

Close your eyes and listen. Turn to face where you feel the wind is coming from. Can you tell?

EYE SPY!

Look around for the movement of trees or the direction of ripples on water.

WET FINGER

Dip your finger in water and hold it up. It will feel cold in the direction the wind is coming from.

Migration station

Learn about these amazing birds and how far they fly to get away in winter.

WOOD THRUSH

This bird migrates from the eastern coast of North America, down to Central America.

GREATER YELLOWLEGS

This shorebird is seen moving to northern Canada in summer and as far south as Argentina in winter!

SWALLOWS

In autumn, these agile little birds fly all the way from Europe to Africa.

ARCTIC TERN

These birds fly from the Arctic all the way to the Antarctic from late July to October.

BRENT GEESE

If you live in Russia, northern Canada and Greenland you will see these birds leaving in autumn. If you live in Europe or the US, they will be arriving.

Draw a turkey. Draw around your hand, add a beak and eye to the thumb, a wing to the middle of the palm and colour!

Berry BINGO!

Autumn is the time of year when berries grow. Can you complete a row of berries? Look outdoors and in shops too. Cross off each type you see.

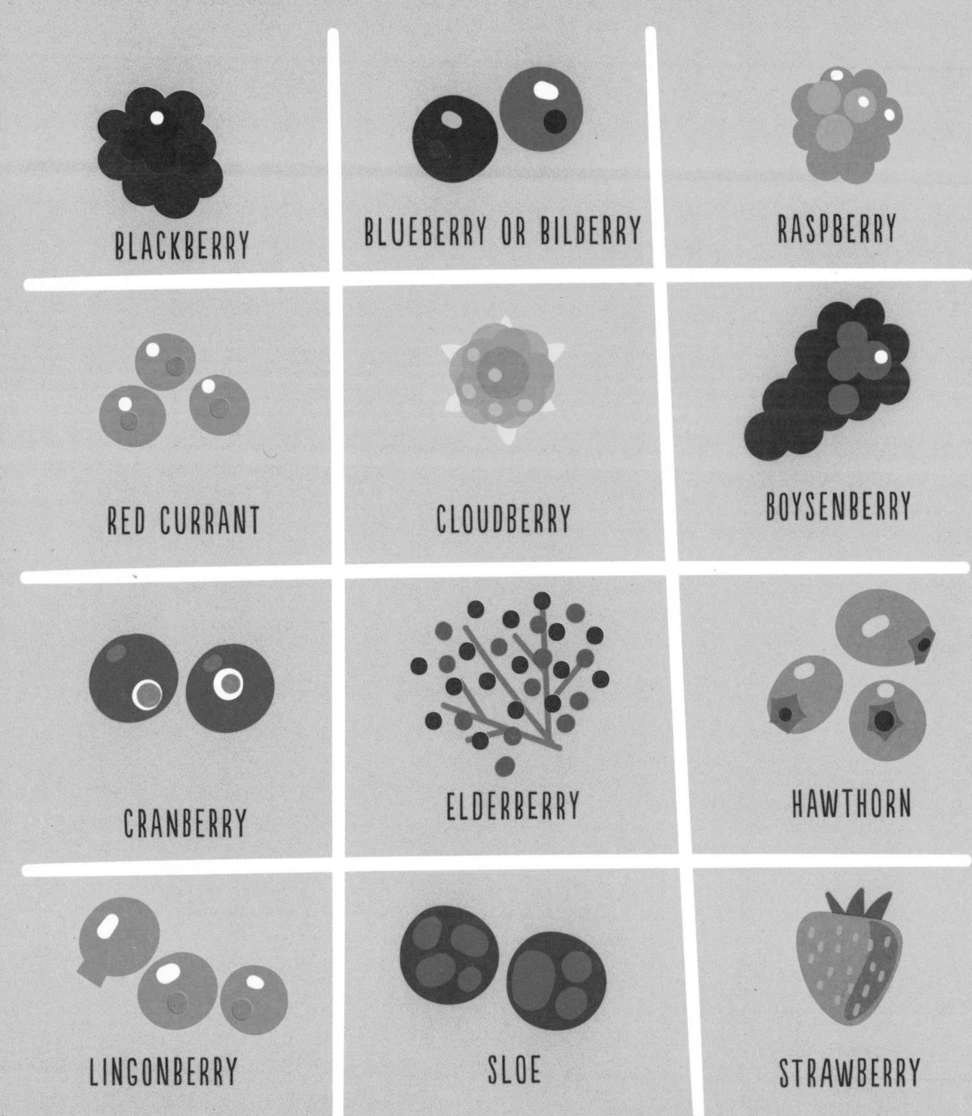

WARNING

Never eat wild berries without permission, some are poisonous.

Superstar

Make these stars from twigs and twine. Hang them in your room or somewhere outside.

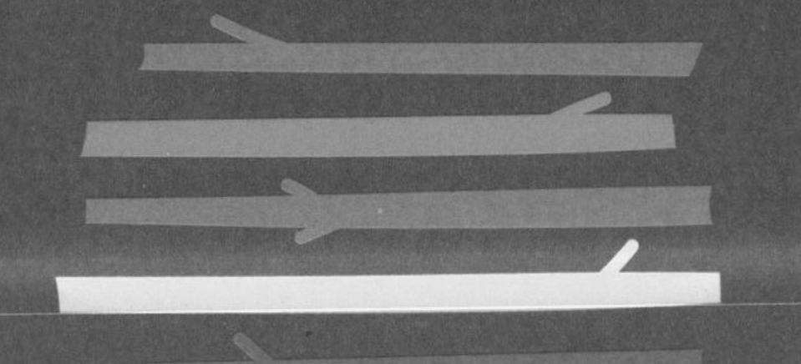

1. Collect five twigs of similar length and thickness.

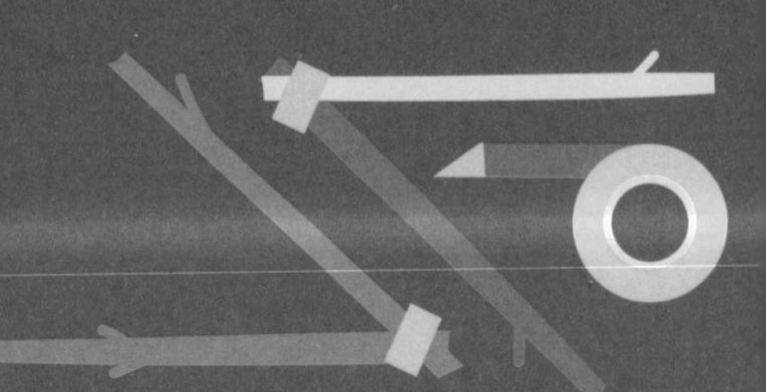

2. Make two 'V' shapes, binding them with tape.

3. Tape together the two 'V's as shown here.

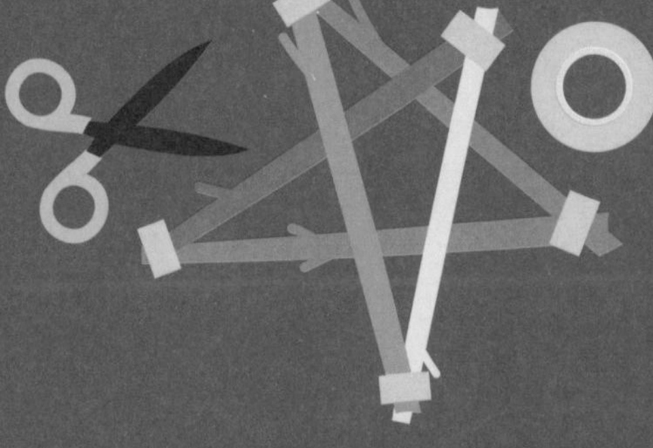

4. Connect the last stick and tape all the loose ends together.

5. Wrap string around the points and centre.

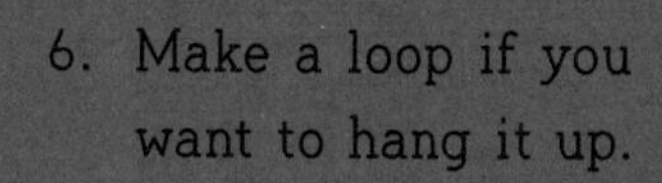

6. Make a loop if you want to hang it up.

Draw your favourite trick-or-treating sweets.

Busy animals

Can you spot animals busy with their winter preparations? Look out for these activities!

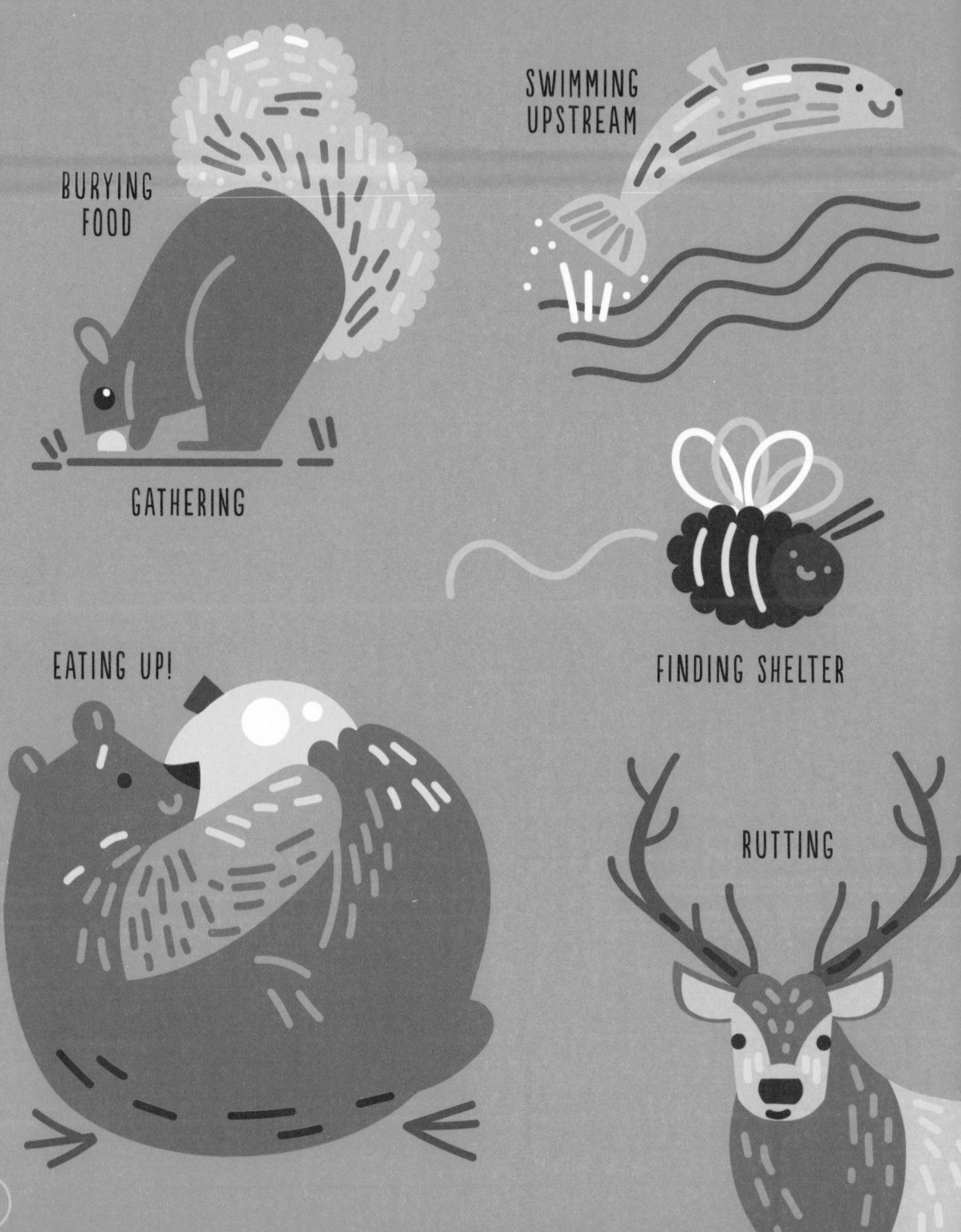

DAILY DARE

Watch a movie you normally would not like.

Under the tree

Fill the park with beautiful autumn trees.

Collect some fallen leaves and dry them out in the sun. Starting at the top of the page and finishing at the bottom, glue your dried leaves in with the stalk end pointing down ... just like a lovely tree!

Light-bulb moment!

Plant some bulbs! No, not those ones ... these ones!

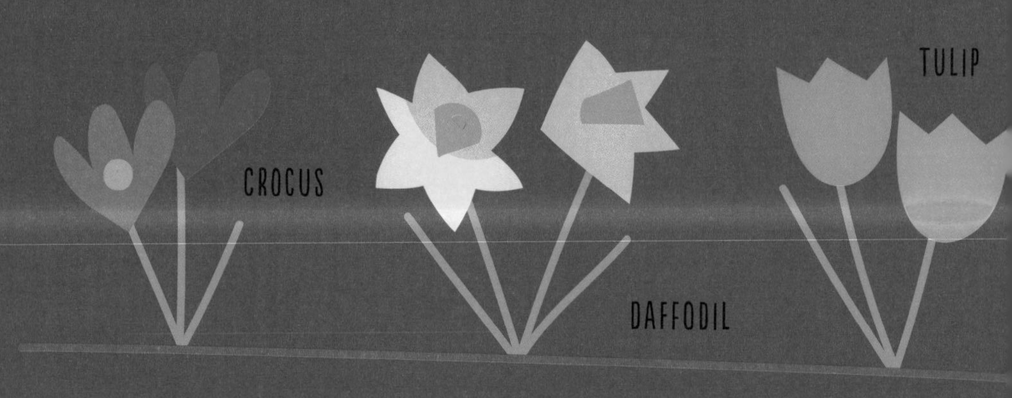

Choose somewhere sunny and not too wet or boggy.

Dig a hole.

Cover with loose soil and pat lightly when the hole is full.

GENIUS TIPS

Pop in this way (not the light bulb way) up.

Do not water unless the ground is very dry.

Draw a creepy monster in one go without lifting the lead of your pencil off the page.

Pop it in the post!

Send a card to spread some cheer or celebrate something special. Try this pop-up surprise.

1. Fold a sheet of A4 card. Score so the fold is nice and sharp.

2. Cut two identical lines into the folded edge, then open the card again.

3. Push the area between th cuts through so it folds inwards. Close the card and press it flat.

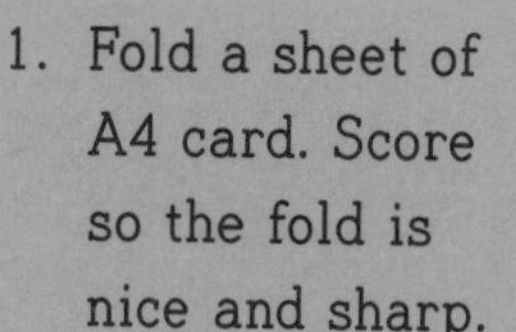

4. You have made the stand for your pop up! Draw your pop art on card and cut it out. Open the card and glue your pop-up art to the bit of the stand facing you. Close the card when the glue is dry. Open it to see it POP! Decorate the front with more cut-out shapes and art, making sure to cover the empty space left by the stand.

Sail away

Learn the International Code of Signals!

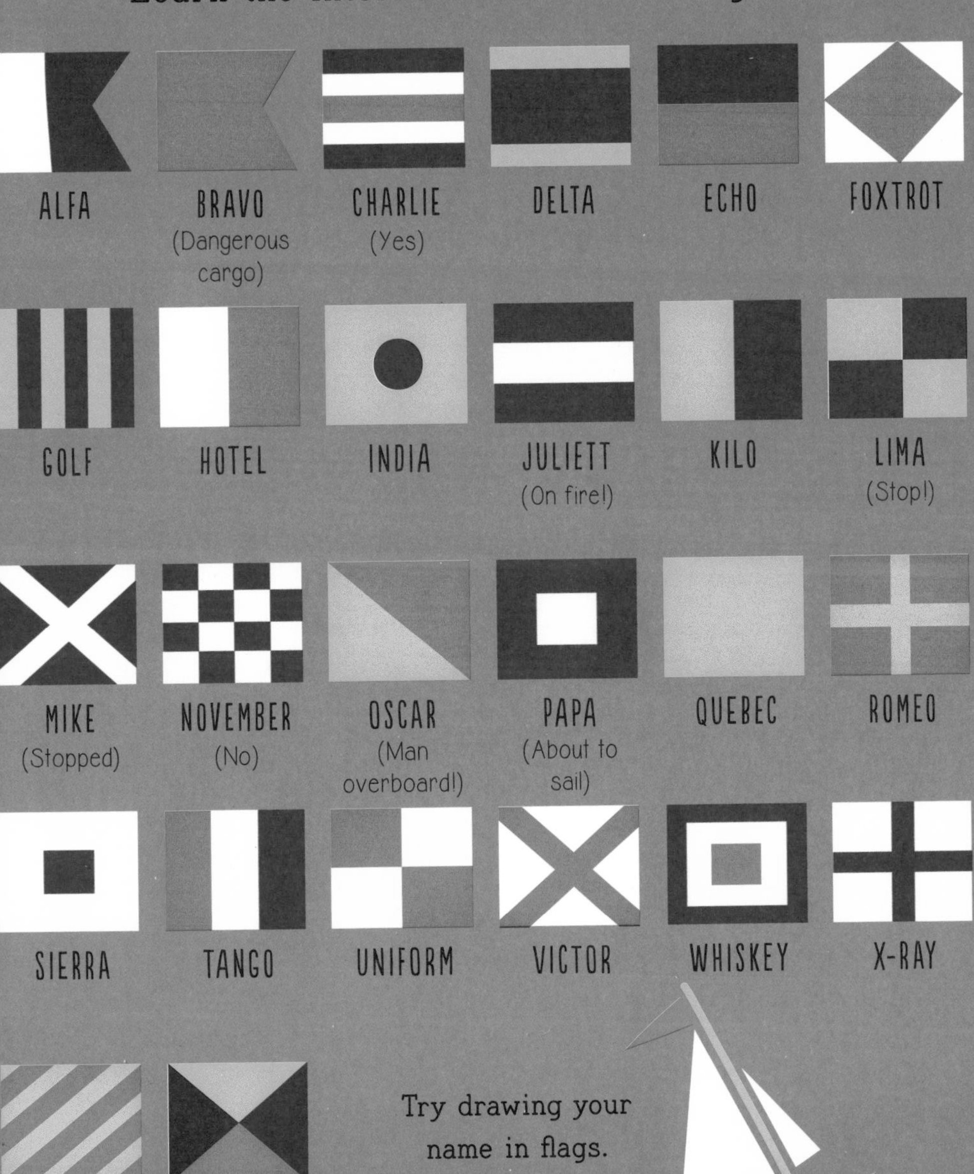

Try drawing your name in flags.

Brain drain

Can you memorise all of the things on this spread? Take as long as you need. Turn the page and write down as many as you can remember.

Do they have
anything in common?
Or can you create
a story featuring
all of these things?
Perhaps it will help
you remember them!

Can you remember all the things from the previous page? Write them down here.

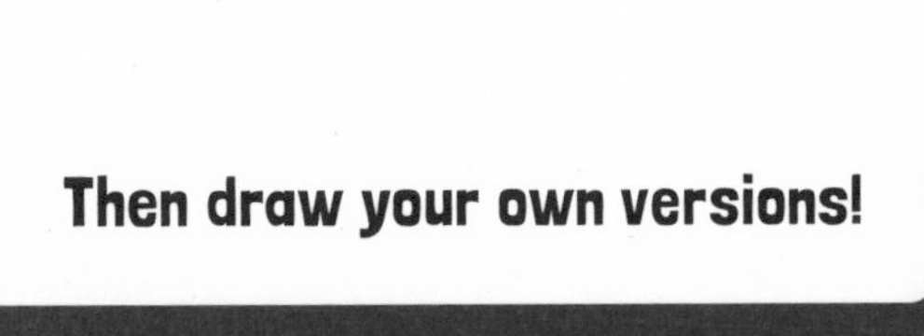
Then draw your own versions!

Autumn lights

Autumn mornings are very beautiful.
Can you spot or even photograph any of these?

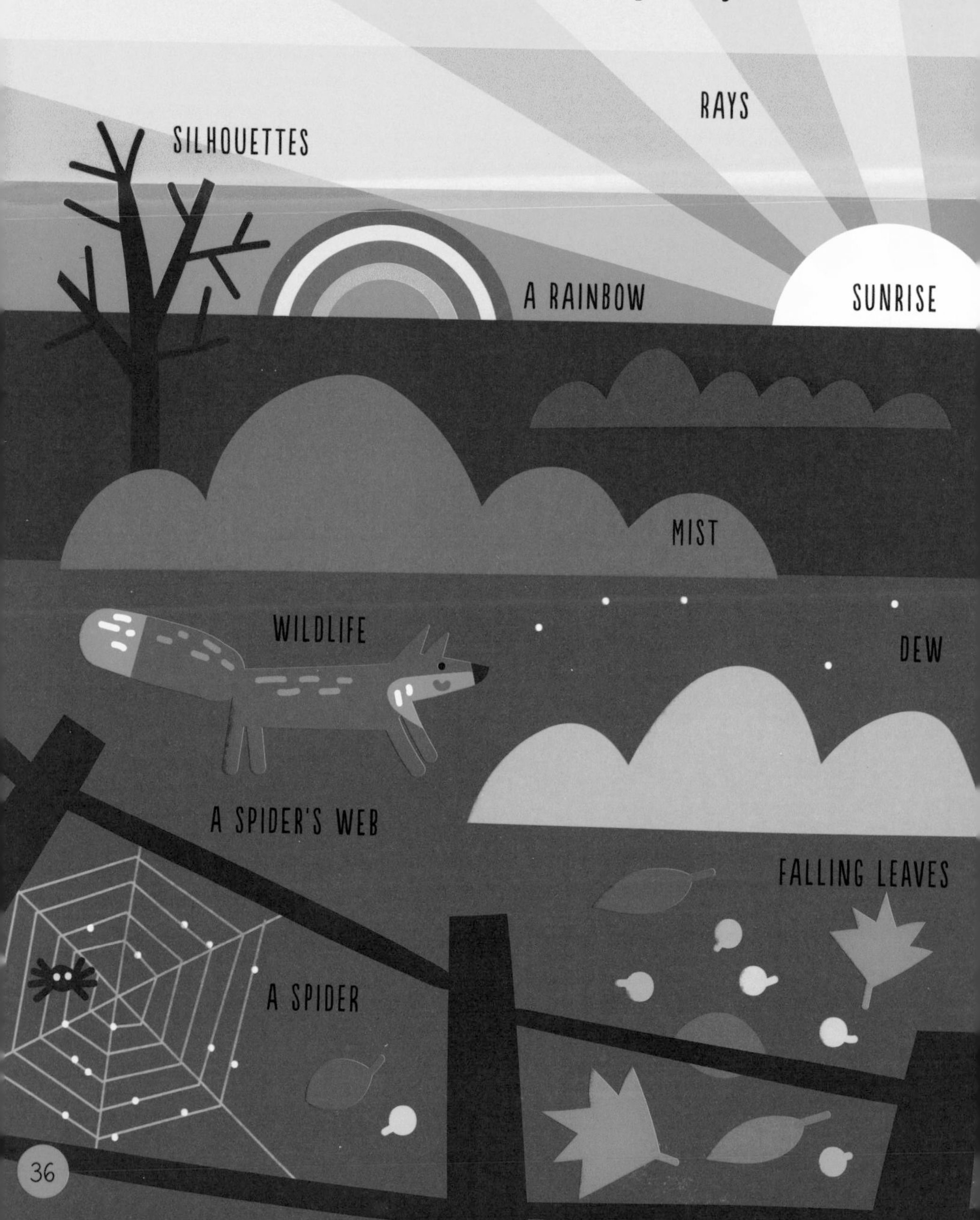

Write a spooky story!

Walkabout

What a perfect time to explore!

Plan a route to somewhere new. Make sure you leave nice and early as it gets dark earlier each day in autumn.

Where to?

....

Why?

....

....

Which way?

....

....

How long will it take?

....

What time?

....

Wild one!

Top tips for keeping any adventure on track.

Spin it

Hold the compass flat in front of you and rotate it until the red end of the needle lines up with 'north'. The compass point that corresponds with where you are facing tells you your direction of travel.

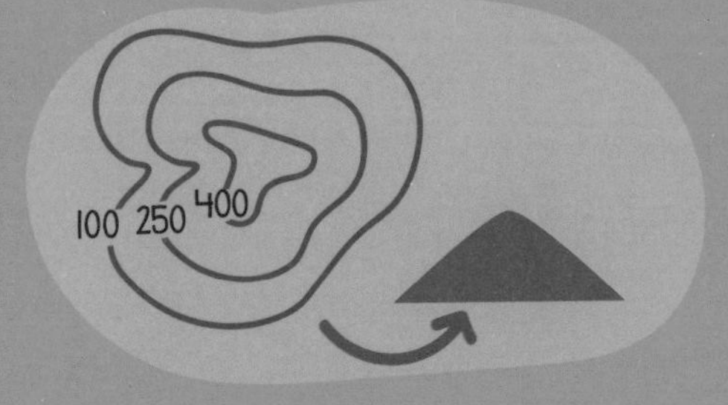

Wibbly-wobbly

Each wobbly line on a map joins together points that are the same height. So lots of them very close together show the elevation (height) is changing quickly.

The wobbly lines are called 'contour lines' and often come with a number that tells you how many metres or feet that point is above sea level.

Stride tracker

Use a tracker or a map to see how far you can travel in ten minutes. Can you work out how fast you are going? How often do you need to check the map?

Eye spy

To find out where you are look for unusual features in the landscape around you. Search the map for them!

Hopping mad

Staying in more makes everyone a little restless! Have a go at this hopping frog.

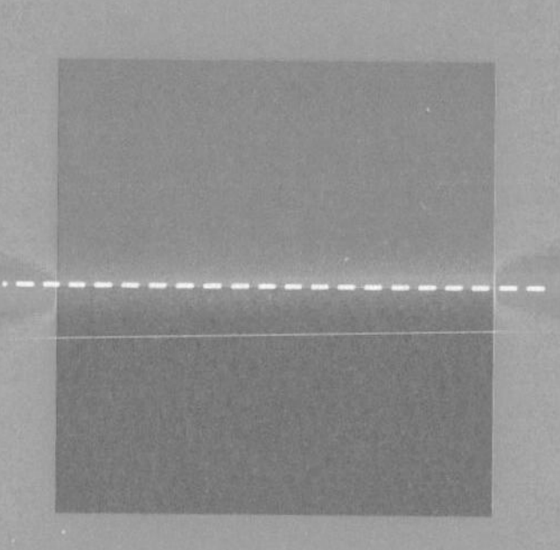

1. Fold in half. Open back up.

2. Fold the other way and leave closed.

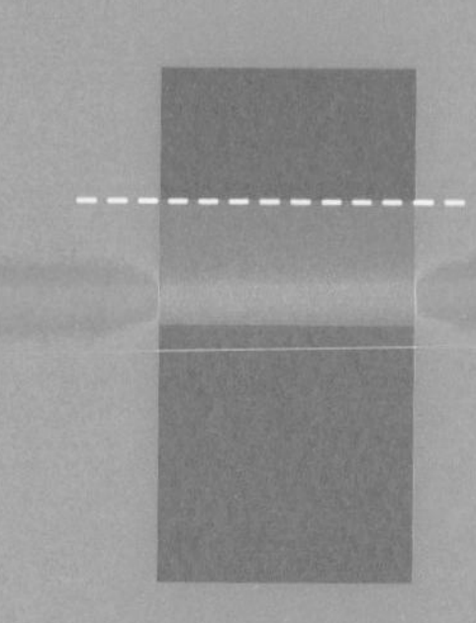

3. Fold the top down halfway. Open.

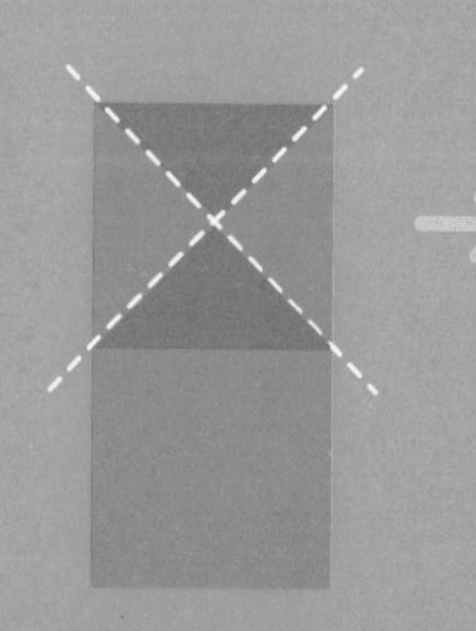

4. Fold and open the top corners one at a time.

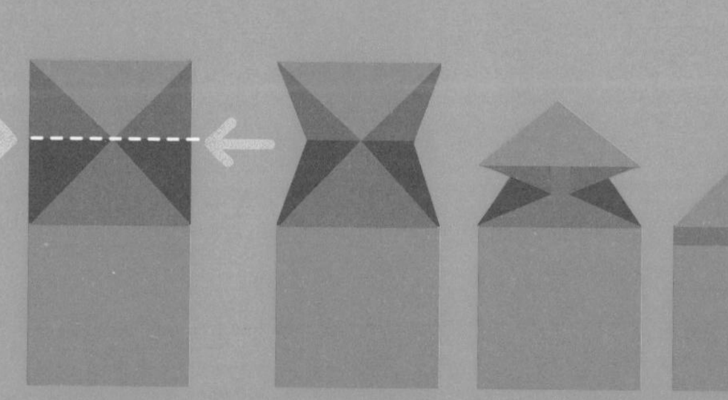

5. Push the sides of the top half in and squash flat. It may fold upside down, but that is OK. Just flip it so the flat side faces down.

6. Fold the free corners of the triangle at the top like this.

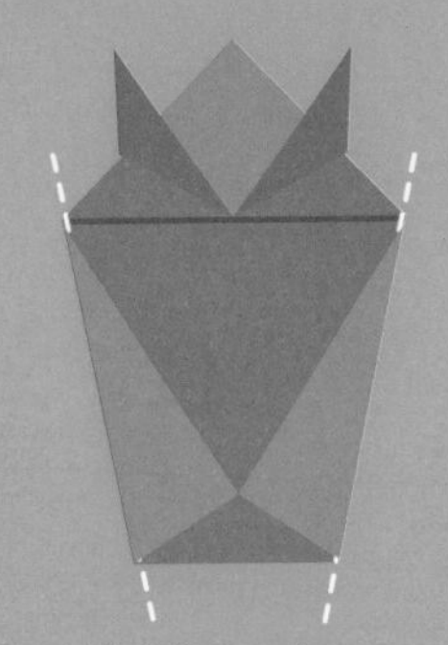

7. Fold in the bottom corners to meet in the middle.

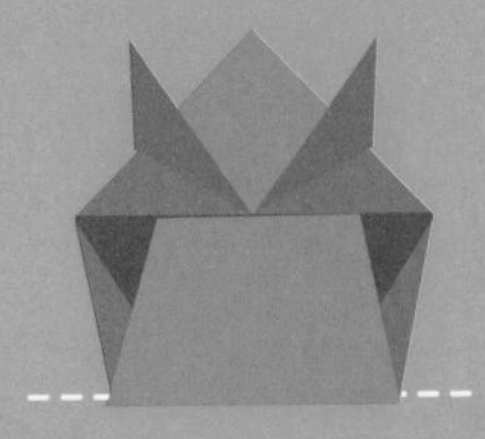

8. Fold the bottom in to meet the triangle base.

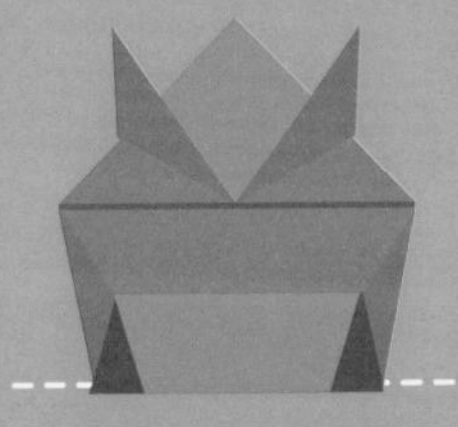

9. Fold back on itself to the folded edge.

10. Turn over.

11. Add some googly eyes.

12. Press down and pull back a bit for the frog to hop!

Fold and score wherever you see a dotted line.

Thought about joining a sports team, club or choir? Sign up and give it a go!

....

....

....

Draw something that bites!

Doodle bugs

Add doodles to these shapes to create some wacky wildlife!

DAILY DARE

Complete the following autumn challenges in your wellies.

Boat race

Make a twig raft! You can race these on a pond, just make sure you start upwind.

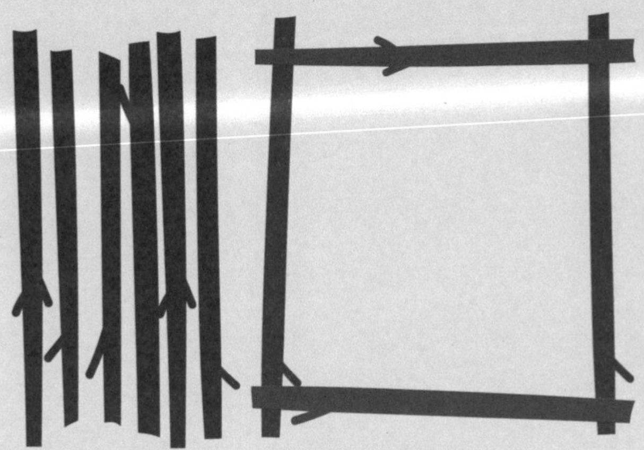

1. Make a square from four twigs.

2. Gather enough twigs to cover the base of the raft. Snap if too long.

3. Secure the corners. Try the knot sequence below or use tape.

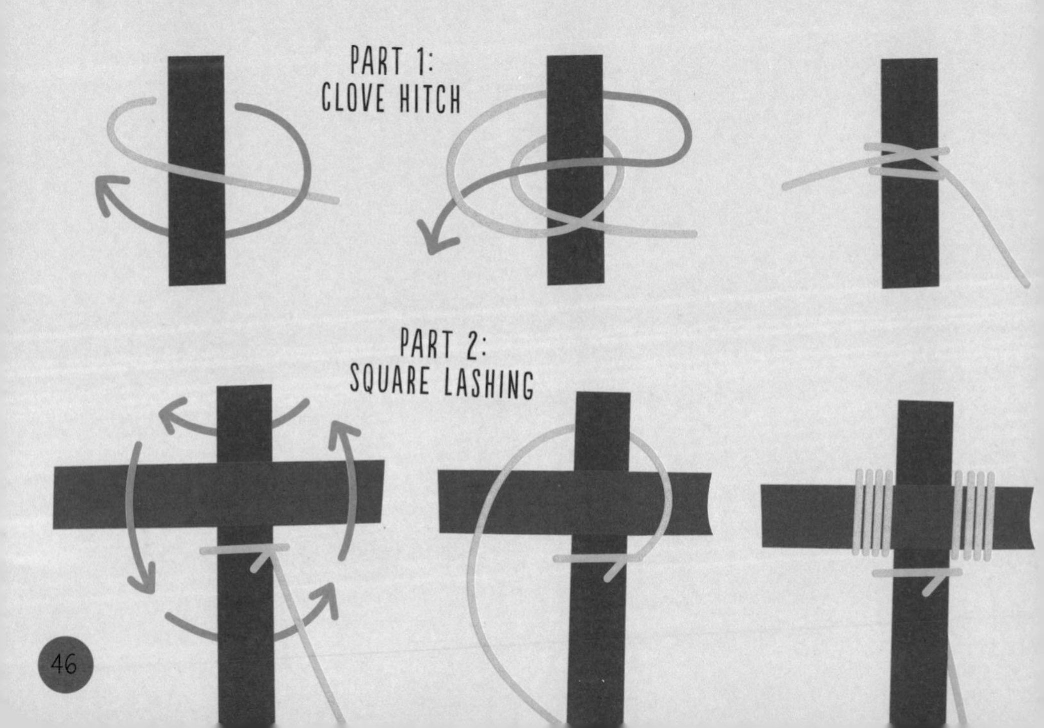

4. Construct the base of the raft by laying twigs on the frame one at a time. Secure with this weaving method, or tape on!

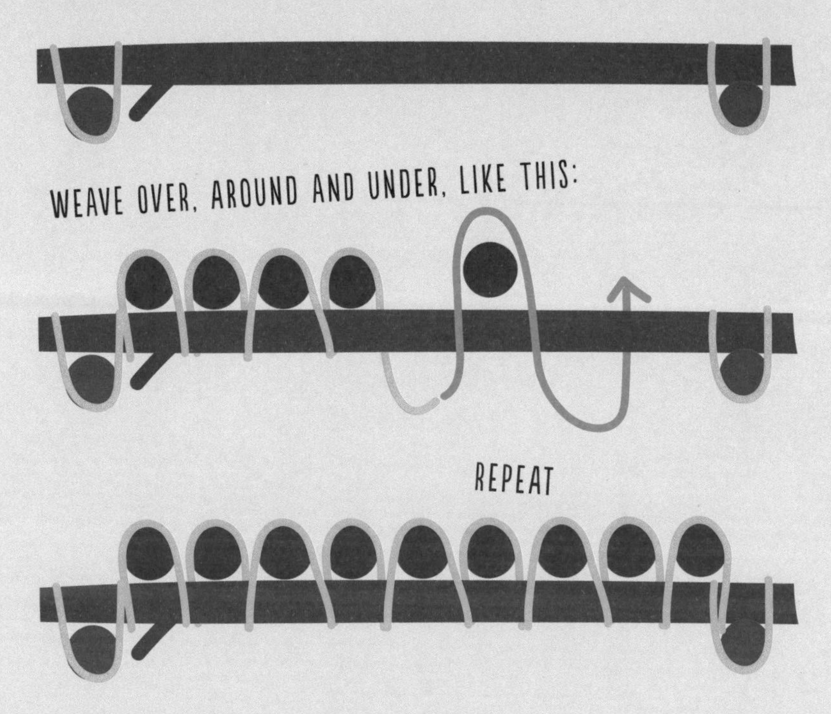

5. Finally, make a sail with a thin twig and a big leaf. Poke the twig through the leaf at two points and push the base into a tight gap in your raft. Ready, steady!

Light up your face!

Try these fun faces in a seasonal squash.
Here are a few to get you started!

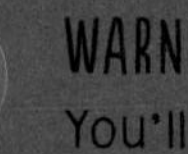

WARNING

You'll need an adult to help with squash carving.

In a pickle!

Autumn is when food is harvested. Some of it gets pickled! But some got mixed up this time. Draw some unusual pickled things in the empty jars.

One, two, tree

Choose somewhere you visit often and track the change in the leaves on the trees.

Tree Where it is:	Doodle it!	**Visit number** 1	2	3	4
....					
....					
....					
....					
....					

Colour the circle in like this:

Use the closest colour you have

Show how many are left

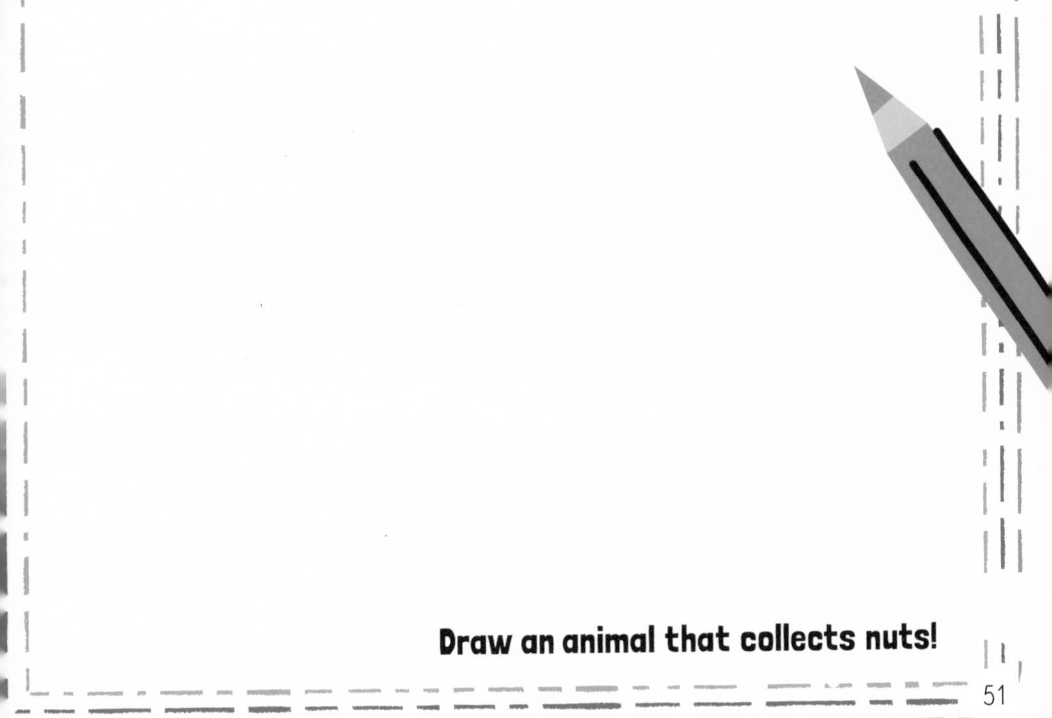

Draw an animal that collects nuts!

Shadow puppets

Create your own light-up theatre with these shapes!

Copy the characters on to card. Attach a twig to the base with some tape. Hold them between the light and a wall to project a big shadow!

TURKEY
GHOST
GINGERBREAD MAN
PUMPKIN HEAD

Write about something unusual that happened today.

DAILY DARE

Rearrange your bedroom!

'Fall' games

Try this parachute experiment.

YOU WILL NEED

1 X NAPKIN
TAPE
HOLE PUNCH
EMBROIDERY NEEDLE
4 X EMBROIDERY THREAD
(each 33 cm long)
SMALL TOY PARACHUTER
SCISSORS

1. Open out the napkin and reinforce the corners with tape.

2. Punch a hole in each corner. Thread the needle then use the needle to pass the thread through the hole and tie with a knot. If you do not have a hole punch, carefully make the hole with the needle.

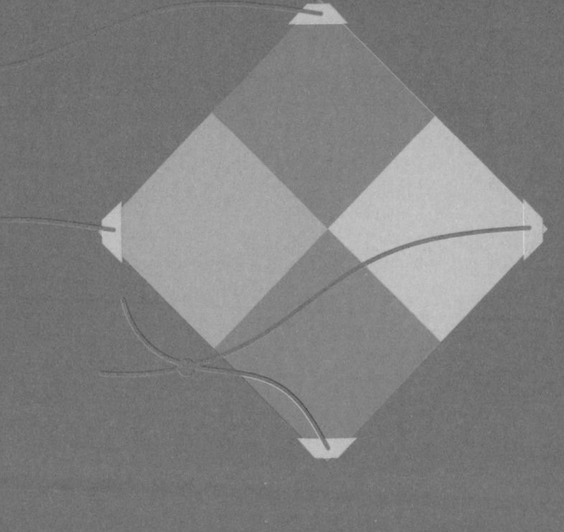

3. Repeat on the other three corners.

4. Tie the two threads from one side together as evenly as possible, leaving some thread at the end. Do the same on the other side.

5. Tie the loose thread around the arms of your parachuter.

6. Take your parachute to a safe high point for launching. This could be a balcony, window or stairway ...

AND RELEASE!

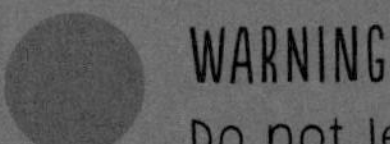

WARNING

Do not lean out or over. Just reach out.

Draw some super-creepy costume ideas!

BOB

Try this apple-bobbing game.

1. Fill a bucket with clean water, leaving several centimetres empty at the top. Put apples in the water.

2. Each player has to kneel down, place their hands behind their back and use their teeth to grab as many apples as they can in one minute. It is trickier than it looks! Keep your hands behind your back at all times.

3. Replace the apples for each person or set up individual buckets. The person who gets the most in one minute is the winner!

WARNING

Always leave your hands free, never tie them.

Un-beet-able brownies

Carrot cake? Pumpkin pie? Courgette sponge? Surely not! Try a sweet recipe full of autumn vegetables!

You will need

UP TO 350 G OF BEETROOT PURÉE
(Cut the stalk off one raw beetroot, wrap it in tin foil and roast at 200°C or gas mark 6 for an hour, or until soft. Leave to cool. Blend with a couple of tablespoons of milk until smooth.)

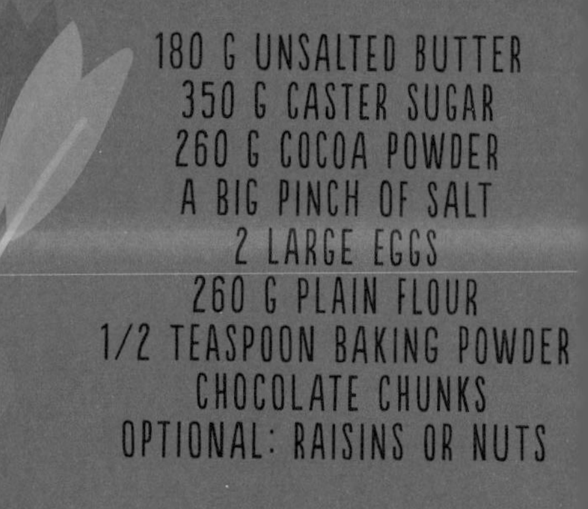

180 G UNSALTED BUTTER
350 G CASTER SUGAR
260 G COCOA POWDER
A BIG PINCH OF SALT
2 LARGE EGGS
260 G PLAIN FLOUR
1/2 TEASPOON BAKING POWDER
CHOCOLATE CHUNKS
OPTIONAL: RAISINS OR NUTS

1. Pre-heat the oven to 180°C or gas mark 4. Line a baking try with buttered greaseproof paper.
2. Add the butter to a saucepan. Stir over a low heat until it is all melted.

3. Using a big spoon, stir in the sugar, cocoa and salt. Leave to cool for five minutes.
4. In a small bowl, beat the eggs with a fork and then pour them into the pan.

Trick or Treat!

Will you get a yummy or a yucky bite!

Make a second batch of brownies, but add a table spoon of curry powder or paprika with the flour. When both batches are cut into squares, arrange them mixed up on the same plate. To play this game, everyone chooses a brownie and shouts 'Trick or Treat!' and then bites into their brownie...
Yay... or Yeurgh!!!!

5. Stir well with the spoon. Add the beetroot purée and mix well with the spoon.

6. Add flour and baking powder. Stir again! Your arm will be tired by now.

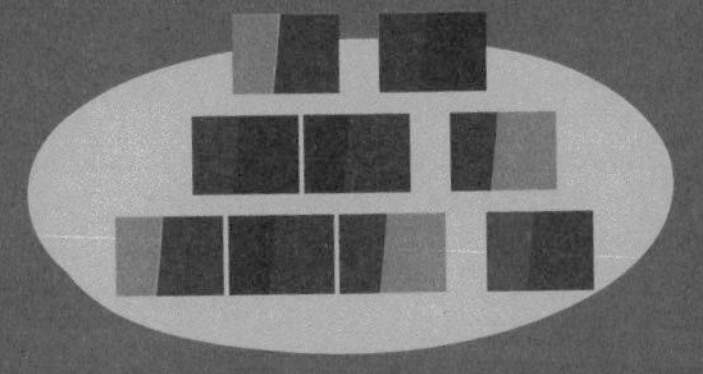

7. Throw in the chunky bits and stir a little bit more. Pour into the baking tray.

8. Bake for 25 minutes. It should feel a little squidgy but not be raw or runny. Let it cool before cutting into squares.

WARNING
Ask an adult before using the hob or oven.

Memories

Write down the best thing that happened this autumn.

Draw something that will help you remember the memory.